Moony Goes on Holiday

Dilys Ross

Illustrated by Mario Onnis

Play Station 1

1 Match.

A astronaut
B moon
C Earth
D spaceship
E clouds
F stars

2 Complete the sentences with the correct words.

| astronaut   clouds   Earth   moon   spaceship   stars |

A There are three .... in the sky.
B You can see the .... and .... at night.
C We live on ....
D You can travel to the moon in a ....
E An .... travels through space.

3 Read, listen and match.

○ bus   ○ cars   ○ footpath   ○ motorbike
○ noise   ○ park   ○ people   ○ street

4 Point at the picture in Exercise **3**. Ask a friend.

What's that?   It's a bus!

Play Station 1

5 Read and match.

○ Moony is watering the garden.

○ Moony is cleaning the house.

○ Moony is climbing a ladder.

○ Moony is looking through a telescope.

 6 Listen and tick (✔).

 7 Listen and say the chant. Then read, match and mime.

A What are you doing?
I'm cleaning, I'm cleaning.
I'm cleaning the house.

B What are you doing?
I'm watering, I'm watering.
I'm watering the garden.

C What are you doing?
I'm climbing, I'm climbing.
I'm climbing a ladder.

D What are you doing?
I'm looking, I'm looking.
I'm looking down there.

 8 Read Exercise **7** again. Ask and answer with a friend.

What is Moony looking at?

Earth.

This is Moony. He lives on the moon. Every day is the same: Moony cleans his home and he waters his garden. Then he walks around the moon. But today Moony is bored. What can he do?

What do you do every day?

Moony climbs up his ladder and he looks through his telescope. He can see Earth. It's green and blue. It looks beautiful.
'I want to go to Earth!' he says sadly.

Look out of the window. What can you see?

Then Moony sees something strange.
'What's that?' he asks.
It's a spaceship and it's landing on the moon.
Moony goes quickly to look.
There is an astronaut climbing out.
He looks nice.
'Hello,' says the astronaut.
'I'm Alex. What's your name?'
'I'm Moony. It's nice to meet you.
Come and see my home.'

Think. Where is Alex from?

'Your home is nice and quiet,' says Alex.
'It's too quiet,' says Moony. 'I want to hear noise. I want to see people. Can you take me to Earth with you, please?'
'OK,' says Alex.
'But remember Earth is big and noisy.
I think the moon is nicer.'

What can you see?
Look and point.

- a chair
- a toy
- some fruit
- a radio
- a window
- some books

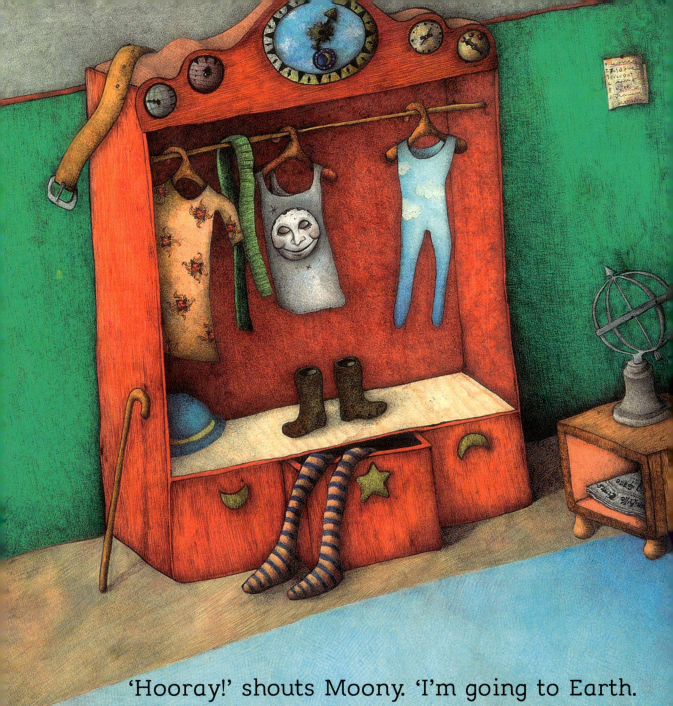

'Hooray!' shouts Moony. 'I'm going to Earth. I'm going on holiday.'
He opens his wardrobe and he puts on his best moon coat.
'Does this look good? I want to look good for my holiday,' Moony says.

Soon they land on Earth.
Moony hears noise and sees people.

Match the word to its meaning.
A forever   ☐ the next day
B is not sure   ☐ always
C tomorrow   ☐ doesn't know

'I love it!' he says.
'I want to stay here forever.'
Alex is not sure.
'Meet me here tomorrow,' he says.
'Same place, same time and I can take you home again.'

Moony walks in the busy street.
There are lots of people but they are not nice like Alex. Some people laugh at him.
They think his moon coat is funny.

Moony sees some people eating.
He is hungry, too. But he doesn't have any money and no one helps him.
He is sad and alone.

Moony walks and walks through the noise and the people.
He sees a sign with big letters: 'Disco'.
There's an open door under the sign and lots of people are going inside.
'What's that?' asks Moony and he goes inside, too.
It's dark and noisy and there are lots of people.
Moony doesn't like it.

He goes out into the busy street again.
There are lots of cars, buses and motorbikes.
It's noisy on the street, too.
Is there too much noise?
Are there too many people?

Close your eyes and listen.
What noises can you hear?
Tell a friend.

Finally Moony sees a little park.
It is nice and quiet. He is all alone.
Moony sits and looks at the sky. He wants
to see the stars and the moon. But he can only
see clouds, clouds and more clouds.
'I want to go home,' thinks Moony sadly and he
goes to sleep.

The next day Alex takes Moony home.
Moony waves goodbye to Alex.
'Goodbye! Come back soon,' he says.

What does Moony like? Tick (✔).
- [ ] noise
- [ ] quiet
- [ ] people
- [ ] stars
- [ ] clouds

'Home sweet home. It's nice and quiet and I'm all alone. No more noise and people for me. I want to stay on the moon.'

Play Station 2

1 Look, read and put the story in order.

The people in the street laugh at Moony.

Moony puts on his best moon coat.

Alex takes Moony home and they say goodbye.

Moony goes inside a disco. But he doesn't like it.

Moony meets Alex on the moon.

Moony sits in a park. He wants to go home.

 2 Look and tell the story to a friend.

3 Complete the sentences with the correct verbs.

cleans
climbs
lands
laugh
shouts
walks
wants
waters

A Moony .... his house.

B The spaceship .... on the moon.

C Moony .... in the busy street.

D At the end of the day Moony .... to go home.

E Some people .... at Moony. They think his moon coat is funny.

F Moony .... up his ladder.

G 'Hooray!' .... Moony. 'I'm going to Earth.'

H Moony .... his garden.

4 Read and match.

○ Drive a car.

○ Go on a bus.

○ Ride a motorbike.

○ Walk in the street.

Play Station 2

 5 Circle the correct word. Listen and check.

- A The moon is noisy / quiet.
- B Alex is bored / nice.
- C Moony's moon coat is funny / hungry.
- D Earth is big / small.
- E The street is busy / sad.
- F The disco is dark / quiet.

6 Read and match. Draw lines.

Adjective	Comparative
big	darker
busy	busier
dark	quieter
funny	bigger
nice	funnier
quiet	nicer

28

 7 **Read, write and match.**

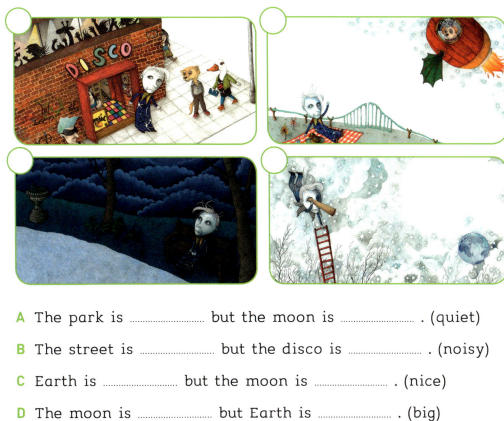

- **A** The park is .... but the moon is .... (quiet)
- **B** The street is .... but the disco is .... (noisy)
- **C** Earth is .... but the moon is .... (nice)
- **D** The moon is .... but Earth is .... (big)

 8 **What do you think? Ask and tell a friend.**

Which is nicer? Earth or the moon?

I think Earth is nicer.

29

Play Station 2

9 Read and match the questions and answers.

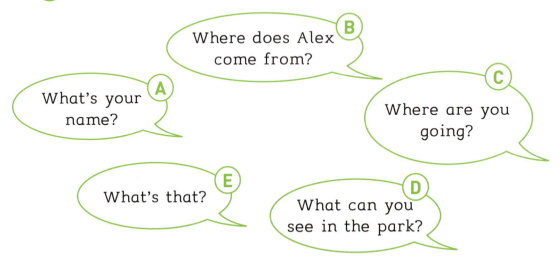

questions

- -

answers

10 Listen and check.

 11 Look, read and complete.

go
go
hear
look
see
stay

A — I want to .... to Earth.
B — I want to .... good.
C — I want to .... people.
D — I want to .... noise.
E — I want to .... home.
F — I want to .... on the moon.

 12 Write a true sentence for you.

I want to ....

....

31

Play Station Project

Model Sun, Earth and Moon

Make your own rotating Sun, Earth and Moon.

You need:

a paper plate

a piece of white card

colours or paints

a hole puncher

three brass fasteners

scissors

1 Draw and cut out the Earth and Moon. Then cut two long rectangles of card. (You can use the templates online.)

2 Colour the paper plate yellow (for the Sun), colour the Earth green and blue and the Moon white or grey.

3 Make a hole using the hole puncher at the end of each long piece of card and in the middle of the Sun, Earth and Moon.

4 Fasten the pieces together using brass fasteners.

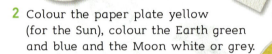

Go to www.helblingyoungreaders.com to download this page.